DISNEY · PIXAR
FINDING DORY

Unforgettable Activities

PaRragon

Bath · New York · Cologne · Melbourne · Delhi
Hong Kong · Shenzhen · Singapore

Odd Dory out

Dory is off on an exciting ocean adventure!
Can you spot the odd Dory out in each row?

1
a
b
c
d

2
a
b
c
d

3
a
b
c
d

4
a
b
c
d

Best pals puzzle

Nemo and Marlin are Dory's best fish friends. Match each piece from the panel to the correct place in the picture. Which piece is not part of the picture?

Answers on page 47

5

Seeing starfish

How many starfish of each colour can you count?
Write the totals in the starfish at the bottom.

....
Red

Yellow
....

....
Orange

Pink
....

Cuddle time!

The otters love a big group hug! Trace over the lines and then copy the colours of the three fur-tastic friends.

Ocean obstacles

To help Dory swim through the jellyfish swarm, cross out all the jellyfish with an odd number. Dory can bounce on top of the rest!

6

2

4

3

5

4

5

1

6

3

2

Happy colours

Bailey thinks that life is a rainbow! Finish the rainbow over his head by completing all the colours.

Marlin's mission

Marlin and his son, Nemo, are searching for their missing friend Dory. Can you lead them through the coral reef to reach the open ocean?

Start

Say what?

Dory speaks whale! Using the key, can you crack the code and work out what she's saying to Destiny?

Key:

A	B	C	D	E	F	G	H	I	J	K	L	M
Z	Y	X	W	V	U	T	S	R	Q	P	O	N

N	O	P	Q	R	S	T	U	V	W	X	Y	Z
M	L	K	J	I	H	G	F	E	D	C	B	A

BLF   ZIV   NB   KRKV   KZO !

___ ___ __ ____ ___!

Dream tentacle

An octopus has eight tentacles. Hank, however, only has seven after an accident with scissors. Design an awesome new tentacle for him here — it doesn't have to look like his other tentacles!

Did you know?
Because Hank has only seven tentacles, he is a septopus.

Get snappy!

Cover each crab with a piece of paper. With a friend, take it in turns to remove one piece of paper from each page. If the two uncovered crabs match, shout 'snap!' and keep the pieces of paper. If they don't, replace the pieces of paper. Keep taking turns until all the crabs have been uncovered and the player with the most 'snaps' wins!

A helping tentacle

Hank helps Dory get around the Marine Life Institute by carrying her in a coffee pot. Draw Dory inside the pot, then colour in the picture!

Fish friends

Just keep swimming!
Draw lines to link these fish into pairs.

Purple path

Dory's parents leave a trail of purple shells to show her the way home. Which path should Dory pick?

Answer on page 47

Chatty changes

Bailey finds Dory and her non-stop chatter really funny!
Can you spot six differences between the two pictures?

Unforgettable friends

Dory has a little trouble remembering things. Help her remember her new friends' names by rearranging the letters to spell them out.

1 K N H A
_ _ _ _

2 T D E N Y S I
_ _ _ _ _ _ _

3 B A L Y I E
_ _ _ _ _ _

4 F U E L K
_ _ _ _ _

Answers on page 47

Seaweed sums

Which strand of seaweed has the most leaves?
Count them and write the totals in the shells.
The first one has been counted for you!

29

a

b

c

d

e

Destination: Cleveland

Dory has been tagged and soon she'll be sent to Cleveland!
Trace the numbers and then add colour to this picture.

22

Pipe pals

Write down every other letter from the spiral below to reveal what Dory is saying to Destiny through the pipes. The first letter has been done for you!

A H D E S L K P J M L E U F A I B N C D F M B Y C F W A R M P I N L V Y Z !

H E L P   M E   F I N D

M Y   F A M I L Y !

Answer on page 47

23

Colourful camouflage

Hank has awesome camouflage capabilities. Add patterns and colours to help him blend into each background.

Pipe path

Bailey is guiding Dory through the pipes. You can help her too, by tracing a path from Start to Finish without taking your pencil off the paper or touching the sides!

Start

Finish

Follow the rays

The rays are going on a long journey. Before they swim away, put the rays into size order, from the biggest to the smallest.

Biggest ⬤ ⬤ ⬤ ⬤ ⬤ ⬤ Smallest

Answer on page 47

Sea lion sums

Sea lions Fluke, Rudder and Gerald need your help with some maths. Work out the missing number in each box by adding together the numbers in the two boxes immediately below it. Keep adding, all the way to the top!

a

2	
1	**1**	**2**

b

		4
1	**3**	**1**

c

	4
1	**1**	**3**

Blue tang gang

Dory stands out from the shoal! Circle her, then see if you can spot one blue tang that is swimming upside down and another that is swimming in a different direction.

Answers on page 48

Character close-ups

How well do you know Dory and her new friends?
Match each close-up to the correct character.

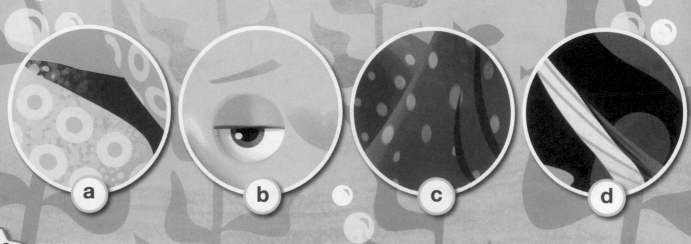

Answers on page 48

Which way?

Help Hank and Dory find their way through the Marine Life Institute by picking the correct path.

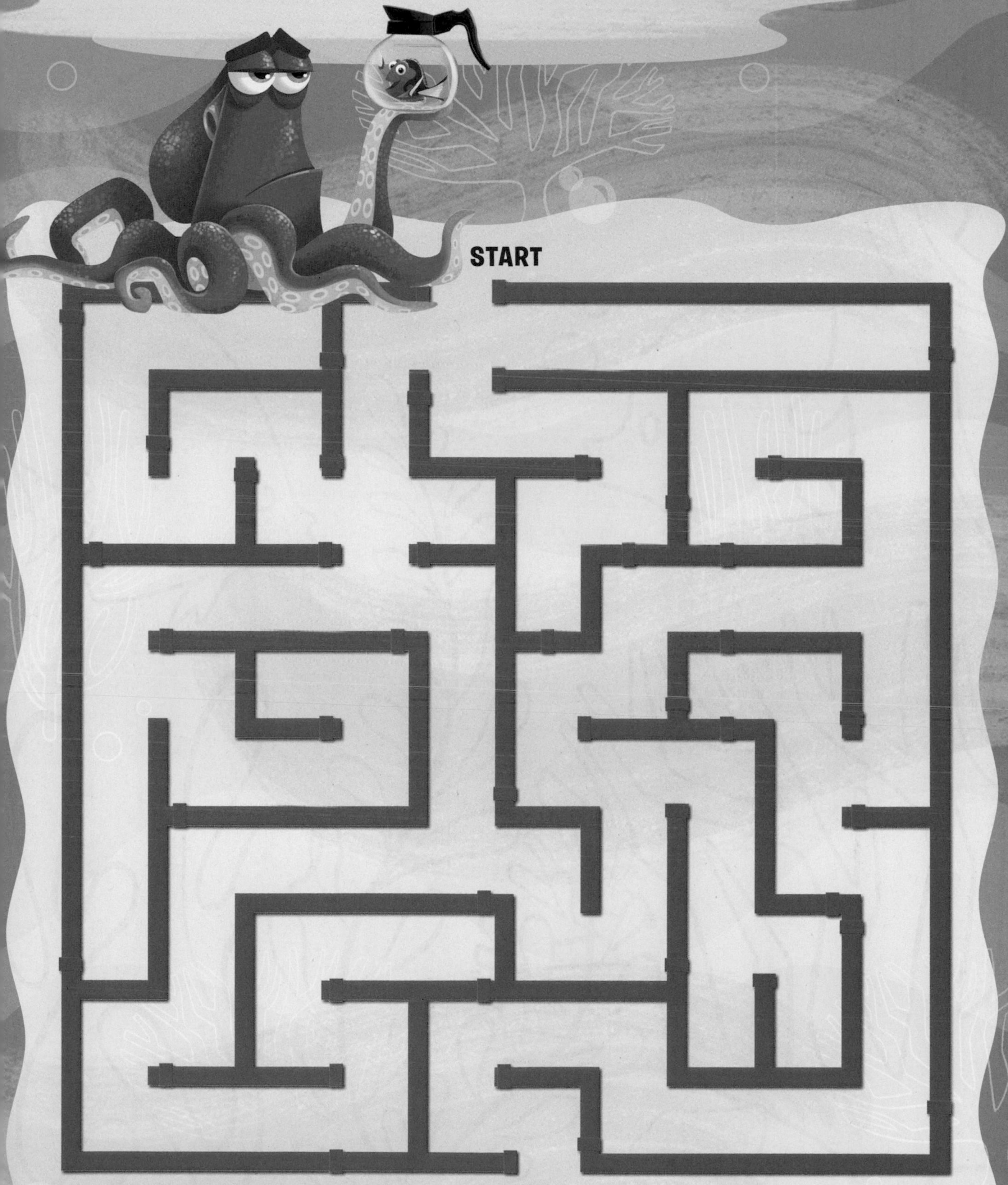

START

FINISH

Create a colourful reef

Give these fish some fin-tastic patterns and then
make the reef as colourful as possible!

Deep-sea differences

Dory is happy to have her pals, old and new, swimming by her side.
Can you spot six differences between the two pictures?

Shell sweet shell

This crabby hermit crab needs a new shell.
Design and colour a claw-some home for him!

Sea sudoku

Can you help Dory and Destiny solve this sudoku?
Each picture should only appear once in each
row, column and mini grid.

Answer on page 48

Bailey the beluga

Draw lines to link each picture
of Bailey to the matching shadow.

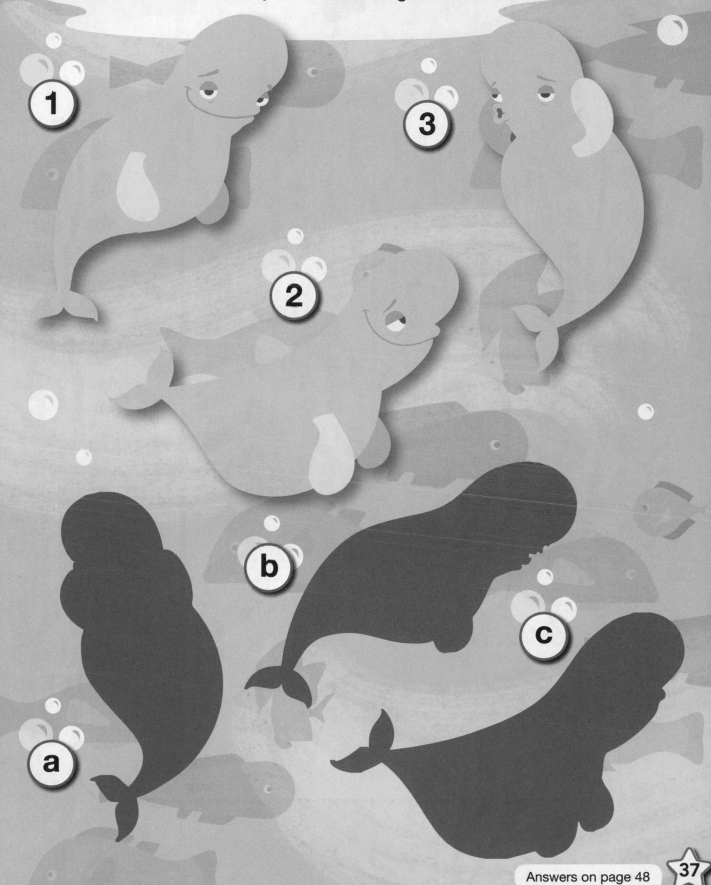

Deep-sea scene

The ocean is a crowded and colourful place!
Can you spot the items from the panels in the scene?

Draw Destiny

Copy the lines inside each square to draw a picture of Destiny, then colour her in!

Whale-speak sequences

Dory pulls some funny faces when she speaks whale!
Can you work out which comes next in each sequence?

Who's hiding?

Can you work out who's hiding here? Write the correct number beside each character in the panel.

HANK   NEMO   DESTINY   DORY   MARLIN   BAILEY

Follow the fish

Lead Nemo to Marlin by following the path
of orange fish through the grid.

Start

Finish

Sea creature sums

Use your super maths skills to solve these sums!

1 🎐🎐🎐 + 🎐🎐🎐 = [ ]

2 🐟🐟 🐟🐟 - 🐟🐟 = [ ]

3 ⭐⭐⭐ + ⭐⭐⭐⭐ = [ ]

Odd Destiny out

Study the pictures of Destiny below.
Can you spot one that is different
from the others?

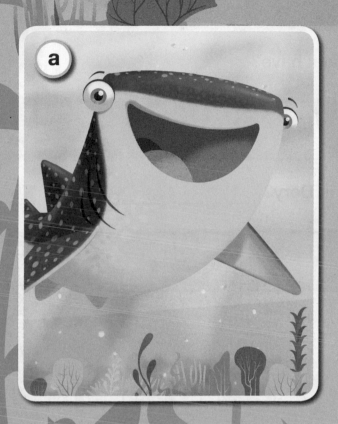

Answer on page 48

Memory test

Are you as forgetful as Dory?
Test your memory with this quick quiz!

1. How many tentacles does Hank have? ....

2. What type of fish is Dory? ....

3. Who is Dory's pipe pal? ....

4. What does Hank carry Dory in? ....

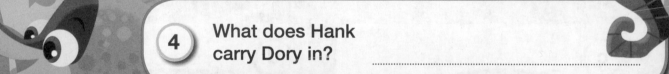

5. Who has awesome camouflage capabilities? ....

6. What colour shells do Dory's parents use to make a trail? ....

Answers on page 48

Answers

Page 4
1 – b, 2 – d, 3 – c, 4 – a

Page 5

Page 6
Red – 5, Yellow – 4,
Orange – 4, Pink – 3

Page 8

Pages 10–11
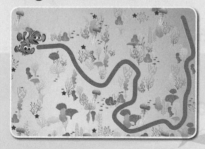

Page 12
YOU ARE MY PIPE PAL!

Page 17

Page 18

Page 19

Page 20
1 – Hank, 2 – Destiny,
3 – Bailey, 4 – Fluke

Page 21
a – 29, b – 10, c – 20, d – 12,
e – 15. a has the most leaves.

Page 23
HELP ME FIND MY FAMILY!

Page 27
f, e, c, d, a, b

Page 28

a: 5 / 2 3 / 1 1 2
b: 8 / 4 4 / 1 3 1
c: 6 / 2 4 / 1 1 3

Answers

Page 29

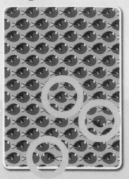

Page 30

1 – b, 2 – c, 3 – d, 4 – a

Page 31

Page 34

Page 36

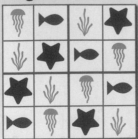

Page 37

1 – b, 2 – c, 3 – a

Pages 38–39

Page 41

1 – a, 2 – d, 3 – c, 4 – b

Page 42

Hank – 1, Nemo – 4, Destiny – 6,
Dory – 3, Marlin – 2, Bailey – 5

Page 43

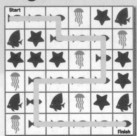

Page 44

1 – 6, 2 – 2, 3 – 7

Page 45

c

Page 46

1 – seven, 2 – blue tang,
3 – Destiny, 4 – coffee pot,
5 – Hank, 6 – purple

This edition published by Parragon Books Ltd in 2016

Parragon Books Ltd
Chartist House
15–17 Trim Street
Bath BA1 1HA, UK
www.parragon.com

ISBN 978-1-4748-5078-0

Printed in China